555
Sticker Fun
Under the Sea

Written by Oakley Graham
Illustrated by Dan Crisp

Licensed exclusively to Imagine That Publishing Ltd
Tide Mill Way, Woodbridge, Suffolk, IP12 1AP, UK
www.imaginethat.com

8 9
Manufactured in China

Blue planet

Oceans cover more than three quarters of the Earth's surface! This vast habitat is home to life at all depths. Add the names of the world's oceans to the map – you may need to look them up!

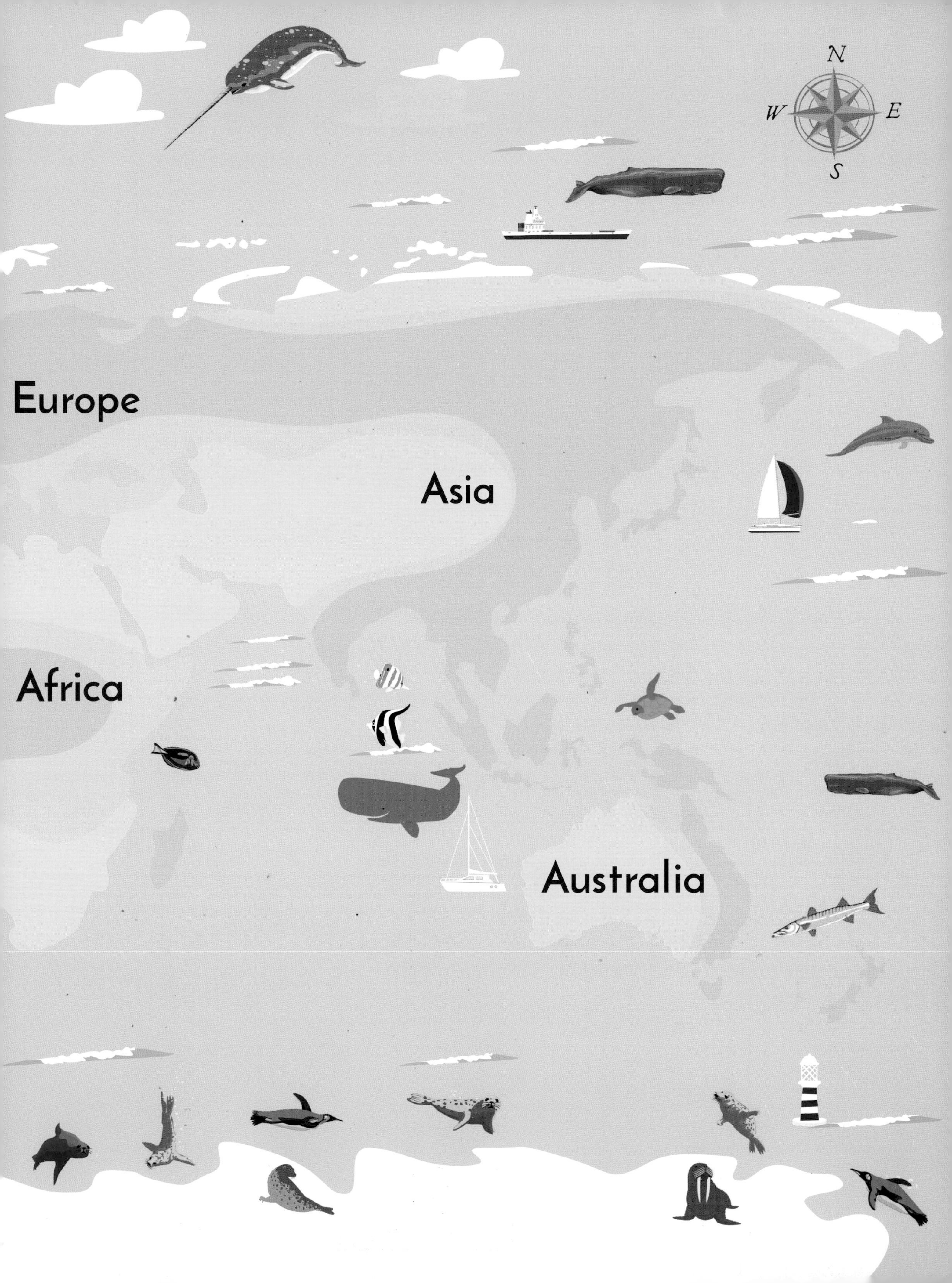

N
W
E
S
Europe
Asia
Africa
Australia

Pacific Ocean

The Pacific Ocean is bigger than all of the areas of land in the world put together! Not only is it the biggest ocean, it also has the deepest trench! Place some endangered grey whales in their Pacific Ocean home.

Atlantic Ocean

The Atlantic is the world's second largest ocean. These Atlantic grey seals are playing close to the shore. Add some more to join in with the fun!

Indian Ocean

The third largest ocean is the Indian Ocean. You can find spectacular rainbow-coloured fish in its warm tropical waters. Find some more clownfish, angelfish and blue tang, and add them to the scene.

Southern Ocean

The Southern Ocean surrounds Antarctica and is the fourth largest ocean. Penguins, leopard seals, elephant seals and male sperm whales can all be found in these icy, cold waters.

Arctic Ocean

Beneath ice sheets and icebergs, the world's smallest ocean is teeming with life! Add more marine animals to this cold Arctic Ocean scene.

The sunlight zone

The water near the ocean's surface is known as the epipelagic zone, or sunlight zone. It stretches from the surface to 200 metres down and most marine animals live in this zone. Make the scene even more full of life!

The twilight zone

You need a special submarine to reach the mesopelagic zone, or twilight zone. It stretches from 200 to 1,000 metres down and there isn't much light. Place more strange-looking creatures onto the scene.

The midnight zone

It is so dark in the bathypelagic zone, or midnight zone, that night and day do not exist! Stretching from 1,000 to 4,000 metres below the ocean's surface, the animals that live here look very scary. Add some more!

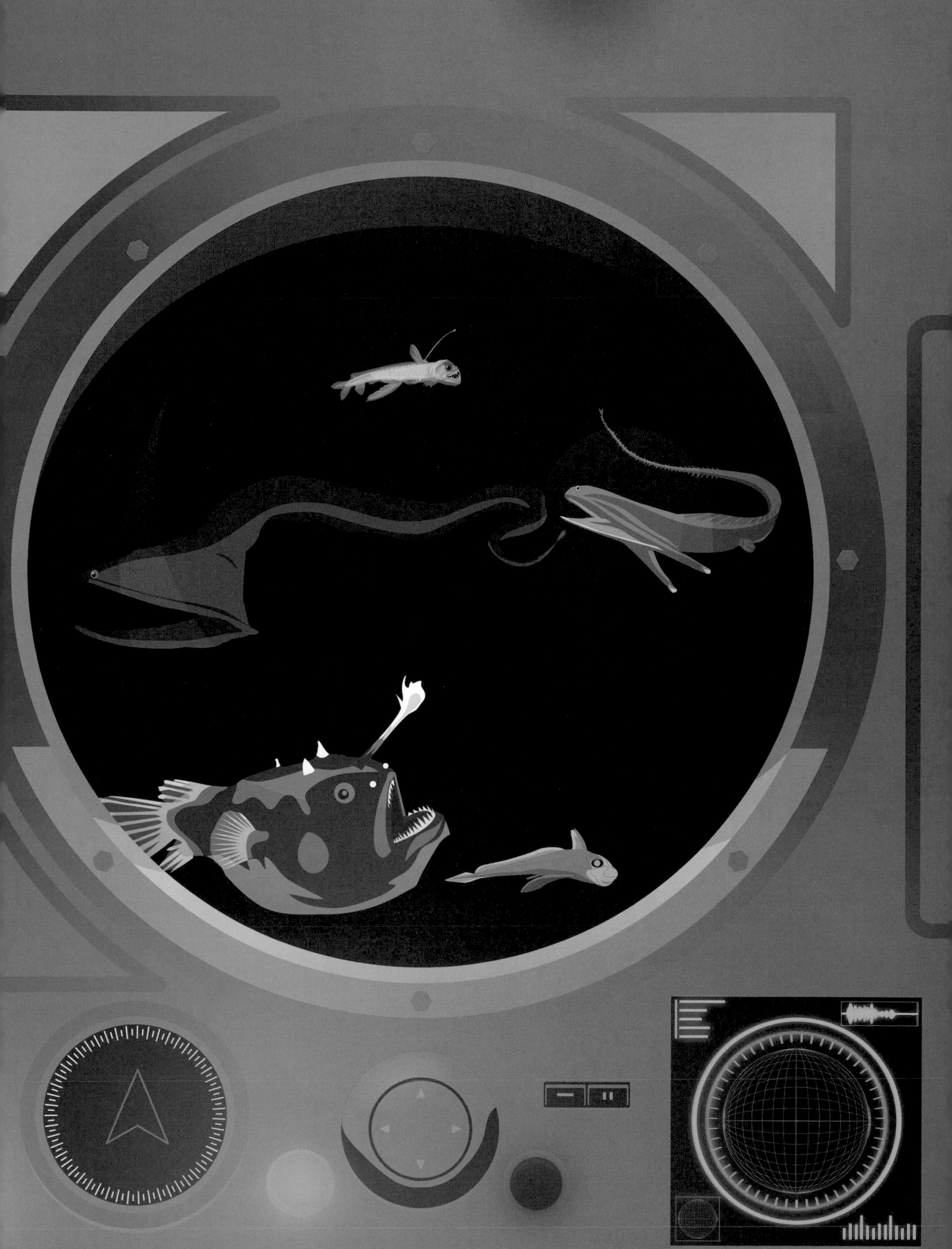

Into the abyss!

At 4,000 to 6,000 metres down, sea creatures who inhabit the abyssopelagic zone, at the bottom of the ocean, mainly feed on dead creatures that drift down from above. Complete the deep ocean scene.

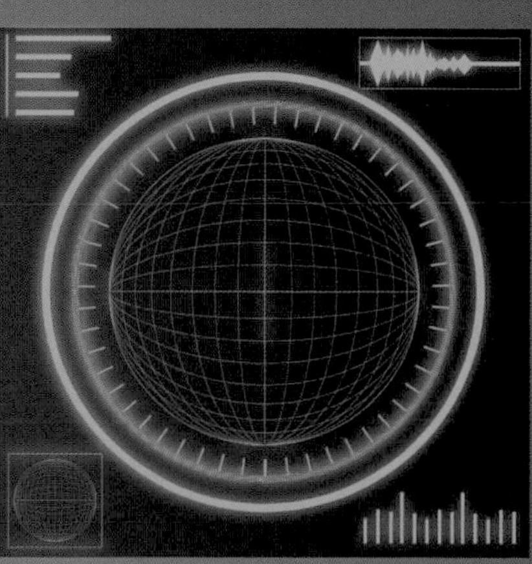

The trench zone

Known as the hadalpelagic zone, trenches in the ocean floor can reach depths of over 11,000 metres! We know more about space than we do about these depths, so add some brave explorers.

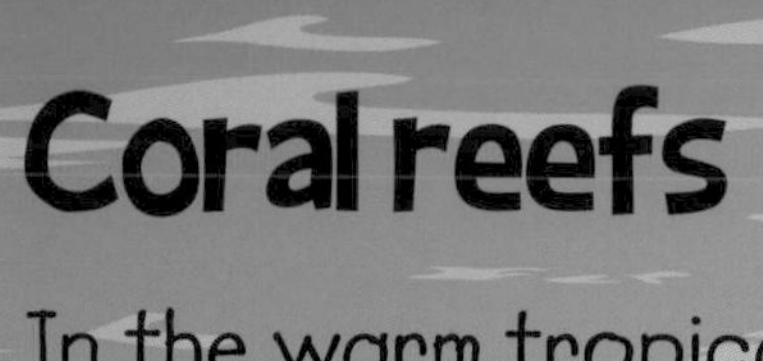

Coral reefs

In the warm tropical waters off the coasts of Africa, India and Australia are some of the richest sea habitats – coral reefs. Complete the colourful coral reef scene.

Feeding frenzy

Sharks have lived in the oceans since long before the time of the dinosaurs. This group of hungry sharks is feeding on a shoal of fish. Add some more to the feeding frenzy.

Playful pod

Dolphins are intelligent marine mammals that click and whistle to communicate with each other. Complete this pod of dolphins as they jump and play together.

Fast fish!

Swordfish, sailfish, marlin and bluefin tuna are some of the fastest fish in the sea. But who will win the race to reach the shoal first? Add more fast fish racing towards their dinner!

Turtle-y terrific

Sea turtles can migrate (move) long distances from their feeding grounds to the beaches where they lay their eggs. Add more turtles and lots of jellyfish to the scene to give the tired turtles a meal after their long swim.

Sea school

Many kinds of fish gather in schools, but few rival the mega schools of herring. Herring schools can contain tens of millions of fish and cover many square kilometres! Add more herring and some predators looking for a tasty meal.

Escape artists

Octopuses can change colour to camouflage themselves. They can also squirt black ink when they need to escape from predators. Add more hiding octopuses to the scene.

Under the sea horses

The male seahorse is an unusual fishy father! The female places her eggs in a special pouch in the male's tummy, where they are fertilised. The young then hatch from the male a few weeks later. Finish the under the sea family scene.

Whale of a time

Weighing as much as 170 tonnes and measuring over 30 metres in length, the blue whale is the biggest animal that has ever lived on Earth! Add a diver, a shark, rays, a squid and small fish.

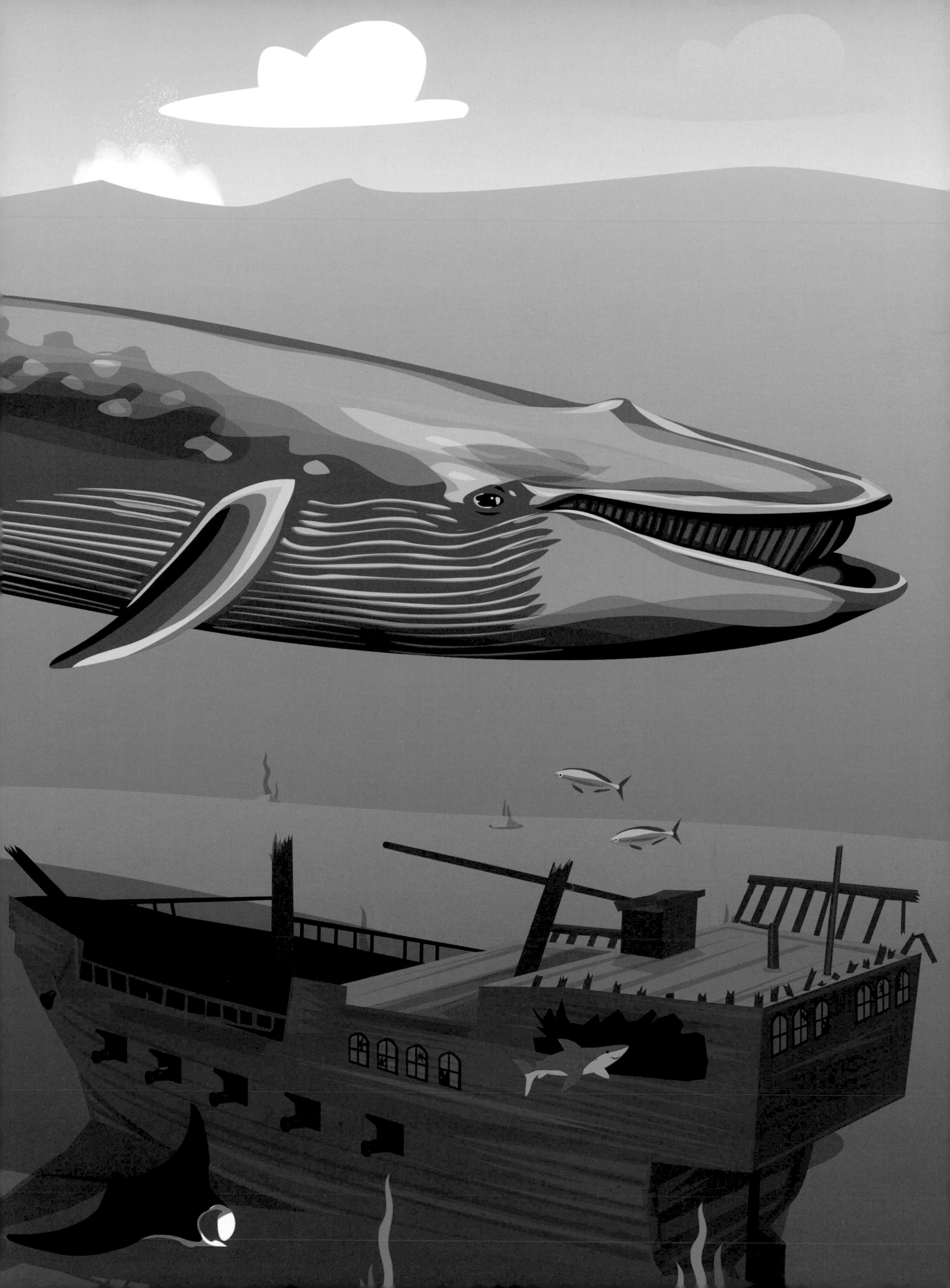

Ocean gliders

Wide bodies and wing-like fins distinguish skates and rays from other fish. Some species live their entire lives on the seabed, while others, like mantas, swim and glide through the open ocean. Add more of each fish.

Ss-sea snakes

Some species of snake have evolved to live in the sea. Most sea snakes are venomous, so watch out when you add more to the scene!

Rockpool

You don't have to venture out into the open sea to discover lots of amazing sea creatures. When the tide is low, rockpools are full of marine wildlife. Add some more.

Great white shark

The main prey for this top marine predator are seals, sea lions, dolphins, sharks and other large fish. What's on the shark's menu today?

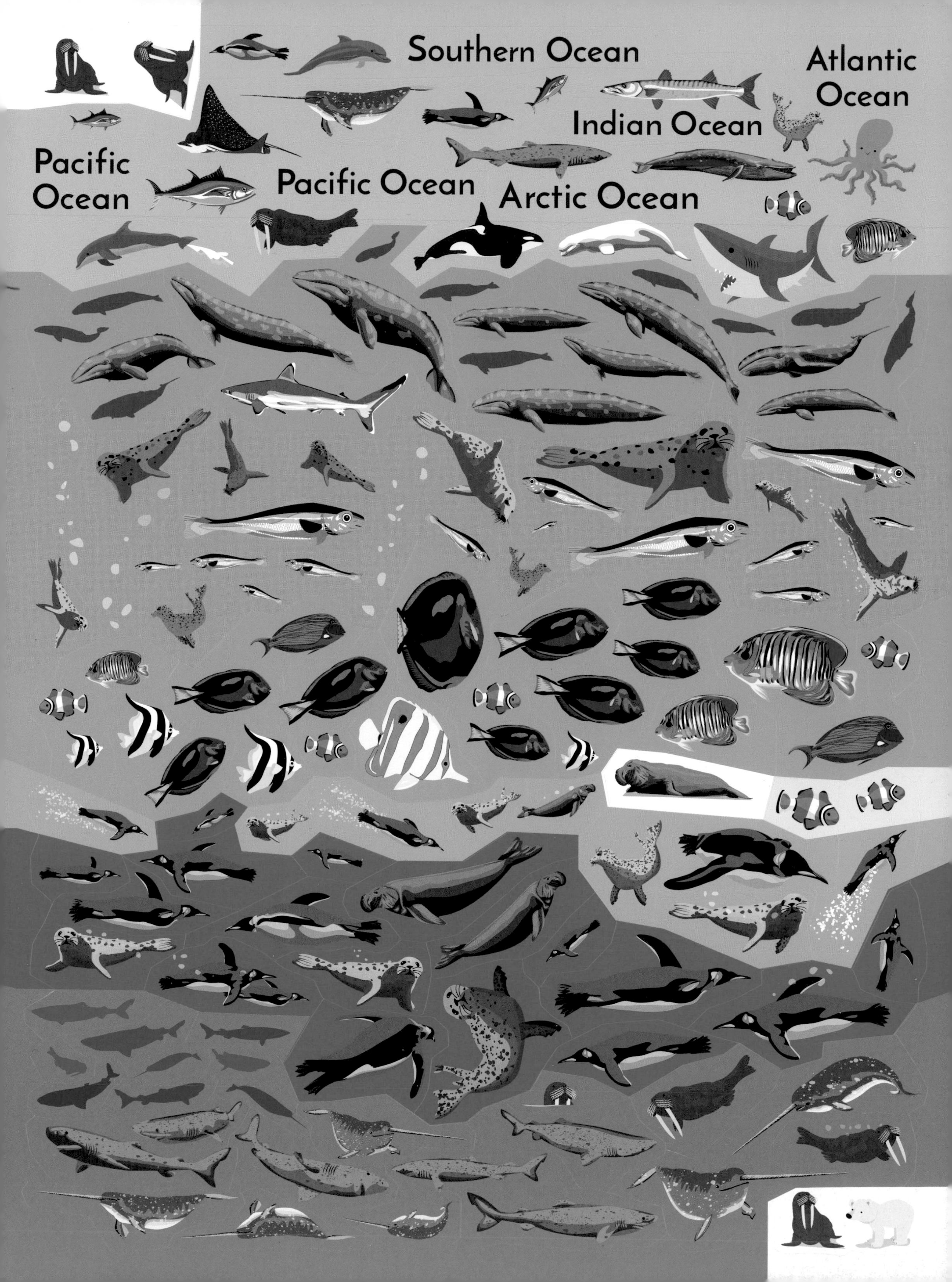
Southern Ocean
Atlantic Ocean
Indian Ocean
Pacific Ocean
Pacific Ocean
Arctic Ocean